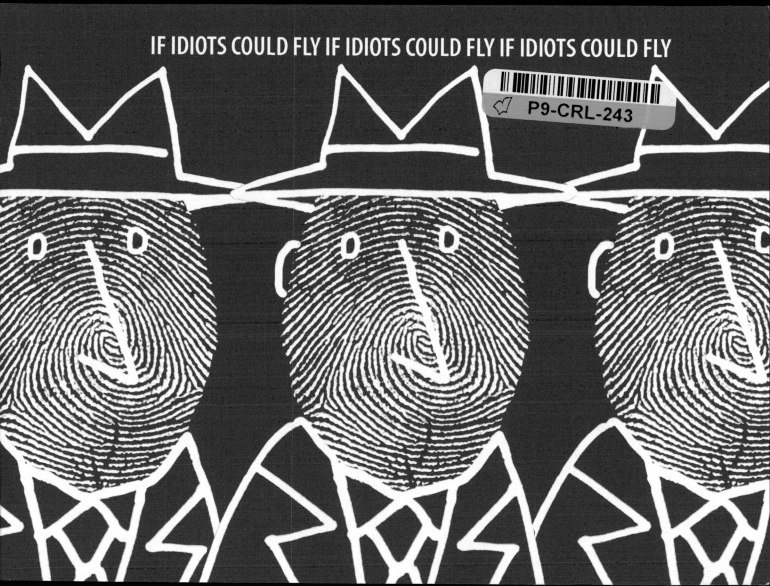

With special thanks to...

This book is dedicated to Chris Peck for his imagination and willingness to take a risk.

My parents for teaching me to think critically and form my own opinions.

And for patiently putting up with the process.

Men In Hats: If Idiots Could Fly
Copyright 2014. Published by
Little Black Book Press and
printed in the good ol' USA.
ISBN: 0-9672865-4-9

To purchase this book
or contact Graham:
**www.grahamsale.com**
**graham@grahamsale.com**

MEN IN HATS**MEN IN HATS**MEN IN HATS**MEN IN HATS**

MEN IN HATS**MEN IN HATS**MEN IN HATS**MEN IN HATS**

MEN IN HATS**MEN IN HATS**MEN IN HATS**MEN IN HATS**

MEN IN HATS**MEN IN HATS**MEN IN HATS**MEN IN HATS**

MEN IN HATS**MEN IN HATS**MEN IN HATS**MEN IN HATS**

MEN IN HATS**MEN IN HATS**MEN IN HATS**MEN IN HATS**

MEN IN HATS**MEN IN HATS**MEN IN HATS**MEN IN HATS**

MEN IN HATS**MEN IN HATS**MEN IN HATS**MEN IN HATS**

MEN IN HATS**MEN IN HATS**MEN IN HATS**MEN IN HATS**

MEN IN HATS**MEN IN HATS**MEN IN HATS**MEN IN HATS**

MEN IN HATS**MEN IN HATS**MEN IN HATS**MEN IN HATS**

MEN IN HATS**MEN IN HATS**MEN IN HATS**MEN IN HATS**

MEN IN HATS**MEN IN HATS**MEN IN HATS**MEN IN HATS**

# MEN IN HATS

**MEN IN HATS began as a doodle on the corner of an envelope** I threw away and then saved, and rediscovered years later. The men had a "Stepford Wives," clone-like quality that I thought might be funny if juxtaposed with silly or esoteric text. I drew about a dozen of them solely for my own amusement.

I never could've imagined they'd get me a job as an editorial cartoonist or that they'd become a controversial socio-political cartoon, featured in one of the country's oldest newspapers, during arguably the most important election in history.

Envelope

The Guys

**Through a series of events in 2010, I found myself in Memphis, TN, sitting in the office of Chris Peck,** the editor of *The Commercial Appeal*. The paper had a long history of award-winning editorial cartoonists. But, slashing budget cuts forced the paper to lay off its last staff cartoonist a few years earlier.

# RISKY VISION

**America was steeped in the upcoming 2012 presidential primaries,** and Chris wanted the paper represented in the national debate by a local cartoonist. Chris learned I'd just moved to Memphis from Los Angeles and invited me to meet him. He was familiar with my commercial work and hired me to create daily political cartoons for the paper. I was thrilled.

**Then just before I left,** he asked if I had anything else to show him. So, on a whim, I gave him five or six *Men In Hats* cartoons (I made up the name on the spot). He studied them and told me that if I wanted to develop them he would feature the series every Saturday - beginning that weekend. I was stunned.

**During one of the most pivotal times in the country's history,** when editorial cartoonists were being purged from newspapers every day, I was being hired to participate in the national conversation - *and asked* to develop a new cartoon series. Wow.

**I was thrilled at the opportunity,** but I felt Chris was taking a risk. How would people react to a cartoon that never changed? People like cartoons because they are simple and quick to read. Would readers put up with all the text in *Men In Hats*? And to be frank, I was just a teeny-weeny bit concerned about having to draw both a daily cartoon along with transforming *Men In Hats* into an editorial cartoon. Then there was the fact that I'd never been an editorial cartoonist before. Chris was supportive and I didn't sleep for two years, but his risky vision paid off. I am proud of the body of work I created working with him

**This book is a collection of *Men In Hats* from 2010-2013** plus some of my favorites that have never been seen before. For those not familiar with my other political or gag cartoons, I've also included a special bonus section along with my favorite hate mail. This book and my other books are available at: **www.grahamsale.com.**

# FOREWARD

Graham Sale has a different take on political cartooning.
Not the same old gags. Not the worn formats of old. I saw
the difference on the first day we met in my office in Memphis.
*The Commercial Appeal* needed to try something new in terms
of political cartoons. And Graham's "Men in Hats" series captured
my imagination.

So in the fall of 2010, *The Commercial Appeal* began publishing a
Graham Sale "Men in Hats" political cartoon every Saturday. The distinctive
panel that always features four guys in hats has become a high-interest
feature of the newspaper.

"Men in Hats" can be controversial. Some people hate them.
Others love the guys. Everyone agrees "Men in Hats" is something new in
a cartooning profession that has grown dangerously predictable.

"Men in Hats" wickedly point out the hypocrisy spewed by many
politicians these days. "Men in Hats" make you think. It's not about
a cheap gag. It is fresh and original. We need that in our political
discourse these days.

Chris Peck, Editor
*The Commercial Appeal,* Memphis

a s d f g h j k l
y x c v b n m

# The Wrath of Con.

One thing I wasn't prepared for was the hate mail I received from right wing Republicans and Tea Party nuts - over *a cartoon!* It wasn't as if I'd mentioned them personally or insulted their sister. Yet, people felt free to insult and even threaten me. One reader called me a child molester. Huh? Many of their letters were printed in the paper.

I couldn't imagine taking the time to respond to a drawing you look at for ten seconds and then turn the page. Yet, some people went ballistic and wrote three page letters - usually men. Others, typically women, prayed for me.

I'M PRAYING FOR YOU.

I'M CANCELING MY SUBSCRIPTION!

YOU HATE AMERICA!

YOU SUCK!

YOU CAN'T DRAW!

A fellow cartoonist was confronted by a menacing man who demanded to know, "Are you Graham Sale?" When he said, no, the man asked if he knew me or how to find me. My friend was pretty shaken. Ironically, these sorts of people react in the same intolerant way as the fundamentalist Muslims they hate so much. But that observation is lost on them. Coincidentally...

My new business cards had just arrived, but after this incident they went straight in the trash. Initially, I was thin-skinned and responded in kind to these letters. But I soon realized it was a waste of energy. So instead, I took greater pleasure getting under their skin. And inspite of their threats to never read me again they just couldn't help themselves.

YOU ARE GOING TO HELL!

SOCIALIST SWINE!

10

# COMMENT

"I'm appalled that you would criticize Mitt Romney for being a liar, when the current President isn't even an American citizen. His birth certificate is a fake. No one even remembers going to college with him. He went to college on a Fulbright scholarship, which means he is a foreigner. When he lived in Indonesia, he was considered Indonesian. This election is over America continuing to be America or becoming a socialist country. The current President said he wishes we didn't have a constitution, so he could do what he wants. He is the puppet of people who want to destroy our country. Is that what you want too?"
- *MV, Memphis*

**"You have a sick depraved mind and need counseling. I know a Christian Counseling Center that can help you. I'll be praying for you. There is a day of accountability and you need to prepare for it, Mr. Sale." - *DM***

"I have spent the last thirty years studying and teaching the word of God. Your cartoon portraying the Lord Jesus Christ as a dark-skinned, foreign-born, anti-war liberal socialist who wants to give away health care and food to the masses, in no way represents the Christ of the Bible. It is offensive. Socialism attempts to make government play the part of the Holy Spirit. There is not a single word in the Bible allowing charitable use of tax dollars. Socialism is anti-biblical."
- *Pastor F Washington*

## MY FAVORITE CON-MENTS:

I won't print the most vile letters I've received. But, these appeared in the newspaper.

"You are an idiot. All you do is lie. You lefties have destroyed this country. And you have a sick mind." ~DK

"Your cartoons are so stupid. How can you accept money for them?" - TM

# COMMENT

## POSITIVE LETTERS from folks who let me know that my contributions made a difference. These were wonderfully uplifting especially during particularly negative news cycles.

"Dear Chris (Peck):

...I know that all too often you are bombarded with criticisms of things your readers wish were different in your paper.

I just thought you might appreciate hearing about something that one of your long-time readers enjoys.

I am especially partial to Graham Sale's political cartoons. His work is not only humorous, but also intelligent and insightful. I've ordered several of his prints and am ordering another."

- Roy B. Herron, *State Senator*, TN

Dear CA Editor,

I want to express my gratitude for your printing the spot on cartooning of Graham Sale. He is one of the very best observers of the national political scene that I've witnessed in your pages going back to Draper Hill in the 70's.

Is he controversial? Is he provocative? Is he doing his part to "comfort the afflicted" and "afflict the comfortable?" You bet he is, in spades. Guilty on all three counts. How great is that?!

He is one of the much needed Liberal voices that this city needs, almost every minute of every day, if it is to totally overcome its moral and social foot dragging.

Jim Palmer, Memphis, TN

# A FEW MORE... COMMENT

...Let me be among the "few and proud" to let you know how much I appreciate your work. It represents a point of view sadly out of favor in thies area. We need more of you given the prevailing political winds. Give 'em hell!" - JS

"Your cartoons have been spot on lately. I look forward to your thoughts and wit and applaud your courage to present ideas that are clearly unpopular in this part of the country." - J Huffman, *retired banker (from the days when banks were honest and provided real service.)*

"Finally, the Commercial Appeal has a cartoonist with courage and an editor with the courage to let him tell the truth. There are many of us who appreciate the fact that someone at the CA has the cajones to stand up to the wing nuts who preach love and family, but actually spew hatred and venom. Mr. Sale's cartoons are a breath of fresh air amidst a swamp of paranoid bible/gun nuts." - Roy G

"My wife and I look forward to your cartoons in each edition of the paper. They speak truthfully and with the force of a thousand words. Your messages speak loudly and clearly. Your work is excellent. Thank you." Ralph S

**"My political views are definitely to the right of yours, but you do have some very smart and clever cartoons. And believe it or not, every now and then you draw something that makes me wonder if my view is correct. You do a great job of getting under my skin, which goes to show you how good you are since this is the first time I've ever responded to a cartoon. Good luck." - David**

"On behalf of teachers everywhere, thanks for your right-on-target cartoon. It is now hanging in our faculty lounge and causing quite a stir! Thanks again." - S Barnett, Elementary School Teacher.

13

# Disappearing Ink. ## The Editorial State of The Union.

**Editorial cartoonists were once a staple in American print journalism** and a rich part of our country's history. Last century about 2000 cartoonists worked for newspapers. Traditionally, cartoonists worked on staff, were syndicated or both. Today, there are only a few dozen full-time staff cartoonists.

The position has disappeared as newspapers downsize, merge or fold. Salaried cartoonists (with benefits) have been dropped in favor of syndicated cartoons, which cost less. But even syndicated cartoonists find they can't make ends meet as they once could.

**A syndication company is basically an agent** who represents cartoonists they think have broad appeal to as many newspapers and news outlets as possible. A newspaper pays a monthly amount to choose from the various cartoonists' work and pays a fee for each cartoon they use. A cartoonist is paid a portion of that amount. The fees are very low so it's a numbers game.

**How low is low?** A cartoonist's cut can be as little as $12 to $35. Some cartoonists report being paid as little as $3 a cartoon. It has always been a numbers game, but the payouts have dropped with fewer outlets to sell to. Those facing low circulation and budgets cuts often ask for a discount, which comes out of the cartoonist's pocket.

Today, being popular doesn't equate with being profitable. It is tragic, and it is not going to get better. Making a living as an editorial cartoonist has become difficult, if not impossible. Even Pulitzer Prize winning cartoonists are unemployed, working other jobs and/or drawing on the side.

**The internet has changed publishing forever.** The speed of technology, cable TV, talk radio, memes, and social media directly compete with cartoonists making it difficult to get their messages out to the public quickly. Who knows what the new face of political cartooning will look like, but as of today, Internet websites are not known for paying artists fairly - if at all.

**MEN IN HATS...**

*B.J. Thomas Kiwanis Singers.*

*Famous last words.*

*Traditional American values.*
*Which ones do you want to return to?*

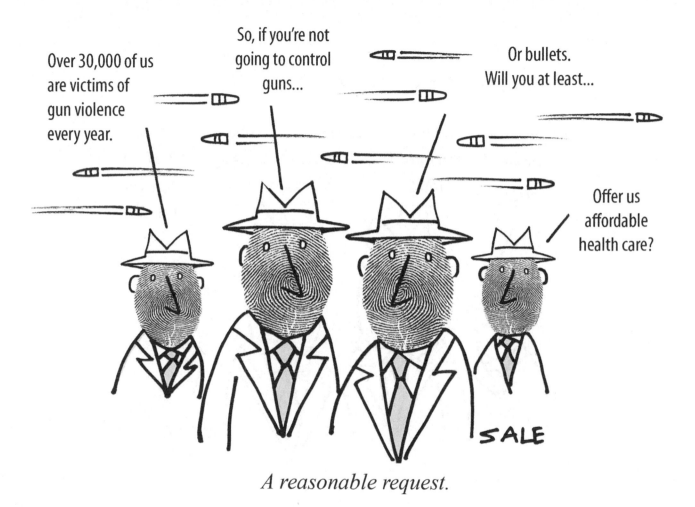

*A reasonable request.*

# What is the greatest threat to marriage?

*If marriage is so sacred - outlaw divorce.*

*What's the real cost of fossil fuel?*

**Reality check:** On 9/11 George Bush banned all air travel, but let two dozen bin Laden family members leave the U.S.A. without being questioned.

Six months later he said, "I don't know where (bin Laden) is, and I don't really care. It's not that important."

Instead, he invaded Iraq who had nothing to do with 9/11 or al-Quaeda.

The bin Ladens have had business ties with the Bushes for decades and invested in Dubya's oil companies.

SALE

*Blood is thicker than water, but nothing is thicker than oil. This is what America should never forget.*

25

Romneyspeak.

*Abominable No Men.*

*The good old days*

*Trusting our future to politicians may be a bit speculative.*

## Obama's a Liberal?

He hasn't closed Gitmo or made adequate financial reforms. He won't prosecute Wall Street financiers and has filled the White House with bankers.

He didn't fight for the Public Option or Elizabeth Warren and still subsidizes big oil. He has expanded drilling rights, gun rights and the Patriot Act.

Sure, he kicked Donald Trump's ass at the White House Correspondents Dinner, but he hasn't legalized medical marijuana and still puts pot smokers in prison. And for crying out loud...

He still thinks John Boehner will work with him.

SALE

*Who's Black & Blue, but Red All Over?*

*Post Traumatic Election Syndrome.*

33

*Republican He-Man Women Haters Club.*

*Republicans: Guardians of Chauvinism*

GOP: "A woman's body knows best."

Creationists are proof that evolution is a work in progress.

Mississippi is the poorest state. Over 20% of its people live in poverty, including 1 out of 3 children.

It leads the nation in underweight babies, infant mortality, abuse, neglect, and its teen pregnancy rate is 60% above the national average.

Sex education isn't required and contraception can't be taught unless "the negative psychological effects of not abstaining" from premarital sex are emphasized.

The governor supports making planned parenthood and abortion illegal.

SALE

*Mississippi Birthing*
*The effect of ignorance on unplanned life.*

*America: No country for sick people.*

*No representation without taxation.*

*Some things aren't as self-evident as you'd think.*

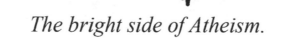

*The bright side of Atheism.*

*How to successfully roll out a new drug plan.*

*It's not a recession - it's a robbery.*

Entitlements, like unemployment make Americans lazy and unwilling to look for work. We need *Makers* not *Takers*.

Corporations are *Makers* and entitled to tax breaks because they *make* jobs. Since 2000 they've *made* 2.9 million jobs...

*Overseas* and eliminated 2.4 million U.S. jobs saving them $2.5 trillion they never reinvested in America's workforce, which is why they received the tax breaks. The average S&P 500 CEO earns $10.6 million a year. Yet...

Over 25 million Americans, are under or unemployed earning $40,000 or less before taxes and without tax breaks.

SALE

*Makers vs. Takers*
*Who are the real freeloaders dragging down America?*

*Unintelligent design.*

**Donald Trump:**
We need to see Obama's birth certificate because nobody knows him until later in his life. Talk to my kindergarten class, everyone knows me.

I have a better track record dealing with foreign leaders. I once screwed Gadhafi out of millions on a land deal.

I go to church when I can. Always on Christmas. Always on Easter. And during the Sundays.

With Glen Beck gone, I worried about who would speak for the raving lunatics.

SALE

**Donald Trump:** *(syn.)* ***ig-nor-anus****, someone who is both stupid and an asshole.*

Froggy went a-courtin'...

*Top Four reasons Newt wants to colonize the moon.*

*Herman Cain't be president.*

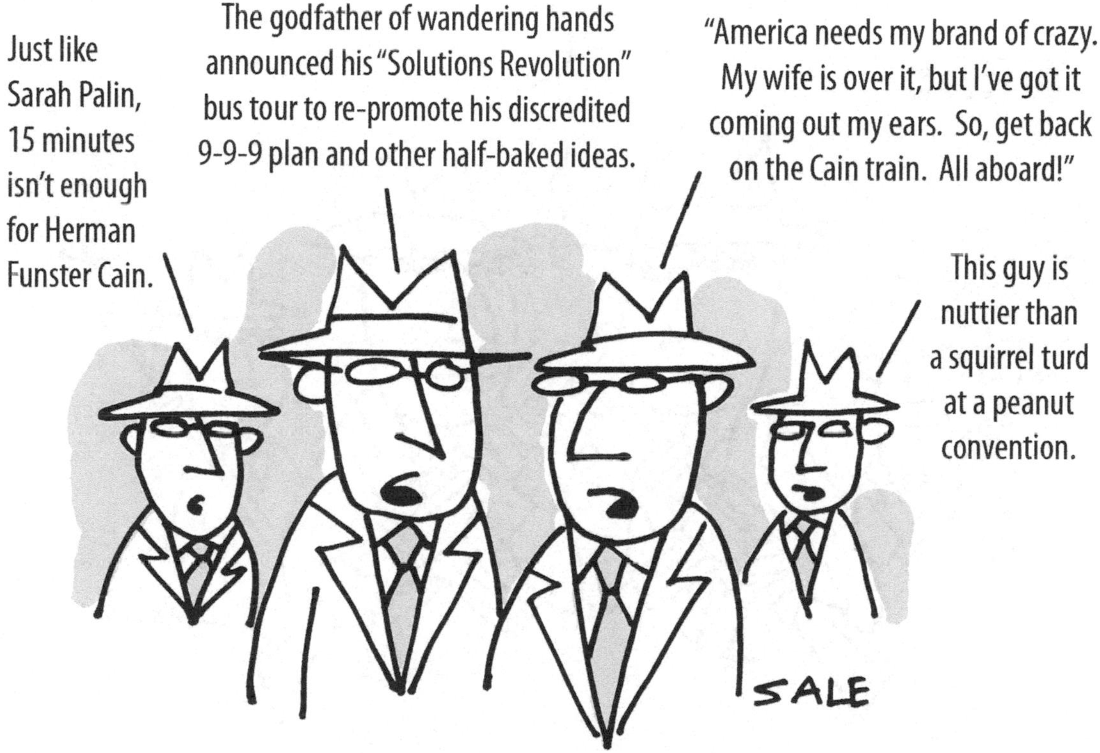


*The Black Walnut rides again.*

# NRA:

*Sending fresh souls to heaven, daily.*

*Wearing a hoodie doesn't make you a hood.*

**Foreclosure is freedom.**
Home ownership is a big
pain, I should know
I have six and there's always
stuff to do.
Rent from us
and relax!

**Rights repress you.**
When you have rights you
have responsibilities. The fewer
rights you have the freer you are.
Let us make you a kid again!

**Unemployment keeps you healthy and fit.**
A job will wear you out. Look at me, I haven't
had one in years and I look great!
Now look in the mirror.

**Politics is awful.**
Be grateful to be
out of the process.
It's one less thing to
worry your silly
little head
about!

SALE

*Republicanspeak: The upside to disenfanchisement.*

Who are the lazy and undeserving?

Fathers, brothers, sisters, mothers, aunts, uncles, cousins...

Friends, neighbors, soldiers, sailors, classmates, co-workers, loved ones...

We remember and honor you.

We want you home.

SALE

*It's time.*

*Billionaires Boys Club.*

How much money do you need for your president to represent you?

*Occupy a postion, Mitt.*

_The Lyin' King._

Mitt Romney: When I'm elected president, I will undo everything Obama has done.

I will make America as it was before he took office. I will reinstate Gaddafi to power, I will send our troops back to Iraq and resume not searching for Bin Laden.

I will repeal laws that inhibit Wall St. and banks from preying upon and swindling investors. I will close GM and Chrysler and fire every worker - *personally*.

Because I love to fire people.

SALE

*Mittmerica.*

**Day1.
Romney-Ryan
Administration
Things to Do:**
Close U.S. borders
and begin deporting
anyone who
looks foreign
or fishy.

Repeal Affordable Health Care, women's rights,
end Planned Parenthood, the Depts. of Energy, the EPA,
student loans, medicare, cut regulations and taxes
for the rich, give Social Security to Wall Street.

Increase foreclosures,
reinstate debtors prisons,
and give Hawaii back to
Kenya.

We love
America
and will suck
out its marrow
to prove it.

SALE

*Cruel Intentions.*

The sound of silence.

The good old days

I miss the days when the world felt kinder, safer, less wicked and angry...

When you could leave your doors unlocked, kids played outside safely, neighbors looked out for neighbors, and summer meant vacation...

When a person's word was their bond, honesty and integrity were assumed, life was affordable, being employed was taken for granted...

And, everyone loved a mime.

SALE

*Days gone by.*

*Different decades. Different goals.*

*The result of dogma on weak minds.*

*GOP & Fox News explain Mitt's poor polling.*

Republicans are trying to institute confusing last minute voter ID laws to prevent "voter fraud."

Yet, they've been caught suppressing voter turn out and purging Democratic- leaning voters from electoral rolls.

To most Americans, "getting out the vote" means helping fellow citizens vote and particpate in democracy.

But, to the GOP it means "getting votes out" of elections.

Shameful.

SALE

*Exorcising your right to vote.*

"If idiots could fly — this place would be an airport."

*Andrew Weiner creates a teachable moment for junk thinking.*

*The liberty to pursue life and the happiness of taking it.*

*Two of life's great mysteries.*

Slavery — another liberal lie

*The dilemma of ideological dissonance.*

79

*Miscontraception.*

Jesus created separation of church and state. Get over it.

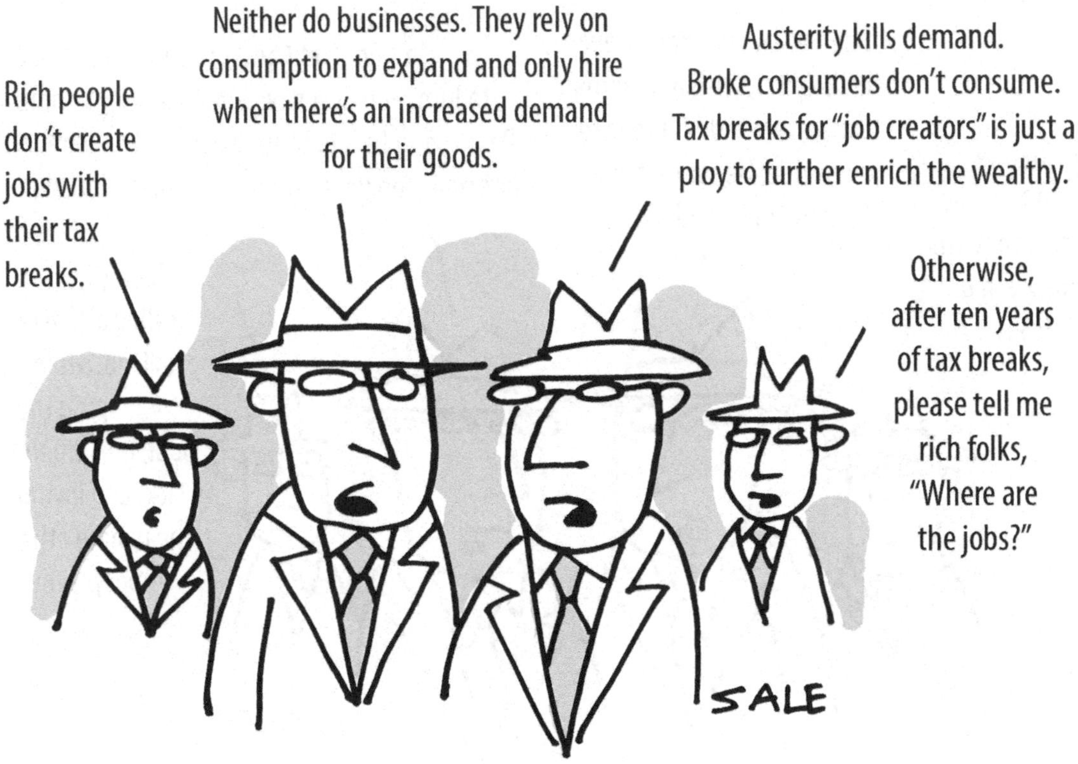


*Job Creationism 101.*

*Willard Romey has never been on your side.*

Bribing politicians was once called corruption. Today it's considered freedom of speech.

Corporations and special interest groups pay lobbyists billions of dollars to get politicians to pass legislation on their behalf.

Politicians respond to their contributors because they are their constituents.

The public should get lobbyists to make policy for them.

Oh wait... Isn't that what politicians are supposed to be?

SALE

*Buy Partisanship.*
*When Money Talks – Democracy Walks.*

Social Security has kept seniors and disabled citizens out of poverty for 76 years—in good times and bad.

It's funded by each of us for all of us and contributes zero to the deficit.

Wall St. gambled away the life's savings, jobs, homes, and pensions of Americans. They haven't been investigated or punished and even gave themselves bonuses with our bailout money.

Does trusting them with the $2.7 trillion Social Security Trust Fund, to gamble with and profit from, seem like a good idea?

SALE

*Social Security is not a scheme - privatizing it is.*

**Dear GOP...**

We are paying you to create jobs, improve our lives, and protect our future.

But all you care about is hurting the President and making him look bad, which hurts us.

You've blocked all legislation to create jobs, stripped American workers of their rights, and displayed a creepy fixation and animosity towards our wives' and daughter's sexuality.

Fight Obama with votes not with our fate.

SALE

*The IRS: 1040 reasons to hate them.*

*America is involved in too many wars.*

*Take that, Fox News.*

Some days I feel I can take on the world. I feel strong and confident, smart and secure in my decisions. I feel the power of my unlimited talents and capabilities surge through my veins.

I feel charming and witty. I'm an alpha male, virile and desirable to women. I'm happy with who I am and where I am in life. I have no regrets and feel certain everything will be fine.

But, most days I just feel like regular old me.

And that is why I drink.

SALE

**Ron Paul:**
I envision an America with no basic services and where only the strong survive.

**Rick Santorum:**
Business can behave immorally, but not people. I'll return America to pre-Vatican II morality and belief systems.

**Mitt Romney:**
I make $57,000 a day without working or creating a single job. I pay less taxes than a secretary, which is perfectly fair and I will say anything to get elected and say it again in French.

**Newt Gingrich:**
I'll colonize the moon, where just as there's no gravity, there'll be no personal ethics or monogamy and marriage will have term limits.

*Obama's Re-election Team.*

John Kerry Debate School: *"Turning swords into pen knives."*

*Have Yachts vs. Have Nots.*

*Warren Buffet's Modest Proposal.*

*FOUR MORE BEERS!*

*My jaw bone's connected to my waist bone....*

*Fry it, you'll like it.*

M-I-S-S-I-S-S-I-P-P-I...S-O-S.

*Bullies are the biggest babies.*

*Wrong. I'm Jesus Christ your savior. Get to know me.*

*Workers' Lament*

*Son of Vodoo Economics*

106

*A simple solution.*

When a panderer doubles down.

*Pretty is as pretty does — and pretty does some odd things.*

*Woes of the Wealthy.*

*The Unjust vs. Just Us.*

*Outsourced and outdated.*

113

*Gunsense. Nonsense.*

## Blind Chinese dissident Chen Guangcheng defects to US:

*After one week in America, Mr. Chen says he is most happy but already sick of the elections, the Kardashians and Tim Tebow, adding, "I could've stayed home and been tortured."*

Republicans signed a pledge to an ideology more certain to destroy the fabric of America and hurt Americans than anything a foreign enemy could do.

They've proudly threatened to destroy the viability, trust and faith in America's economy to achieve their political ends.

They've vowed to fight everything the president proposes and refused to negotiate on behalf of ordinary Americans if it hurts their wealthy contributors.

What's happened to the real Republican Party and how do we get them back?

SALE

*Invasion of the Party Snatchers.*

*The Full Romney.*

*Most Influential Person of 2012.*

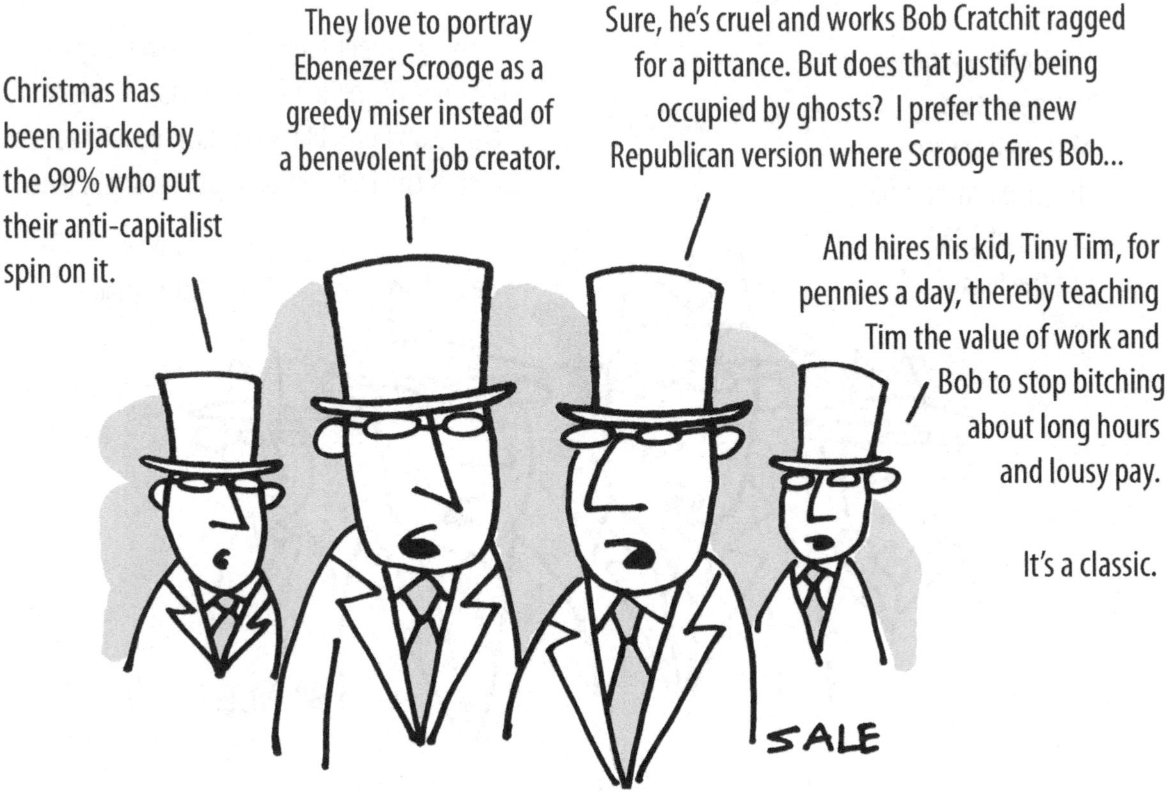


*A Republican Christmas Carol.*

HOW IT GOT STARTED. HOW IT GOT STARTED. HOW IT GOT STARTED.
HOW IT GOT STARTED. HO    GOT      ED. HOW IT GOT STARTED.
HOW IT GOT STARTED. HO         ED. HOW IT GOT STARTED.
HOW IT GOT STARTED.                HOW IT GOT STARTED.
HOW IT GOT STARTED.                HOW IT GOT STARTED.
HOW IT GOT STARTED.                HOW IT GOT STARTED.
HOW IT GOT STARTED.                HOW IT GOT STARTED.
HOW IT GOT STARTED.                HOW IT GOT STARTED.
HOW IT GOT STARTED.                HOW IT GOT STARTED.
HOW IT GOT STARTED.                HOW IT GOT STARTED.
HOW IT GOT STARTED.                HOW IT GOT STARTED.
HOW IT GOT STARTED.                HOW IT GOT STARTED.
HOW IT GOT STA                     HOW IT GOT STARTED.
HOW IT GOT ST                      HOW IT GOT STARTED.

*Great questions of our time.*

*Liars Club.  #101*

*Liars Club. #102*

*Liars Club.  #103*

*Liars Club. #104*

*Dust mites roasting on an open fire.*

*Everyone loves Lolly. Lolly is made of cheese.*

*Board of Rhetorical Questions.*

*Phone Shui.*

**I love you.**

All you need is love.

Love is the answer.

You only hurt the one you love.

I love your sister.

*Love stinks.*

*The reality of fantasy.*

*Thoughts of the Thought Police.*

**Sold on Sale.**

I just want to say how much I enjoy Graham Sale's cartoons. He is so good at making his point and showing the absurdity of certain situations. Despite the vitriolic rants against him, Sale is always right on the money. This part of the country needs his insights. I'm glad we have him. - Julie R.

Graham, my wife and I look for your cartoons in each edition of the paper. They speak truthfully and with the force of a thousand words. Even those among us who don't think for themselves should get the message loud and clear. Keep up the excellent work.
- Thank you, Ralph

**"Hats" fits the mood of America.**
Graham Sale's "Men in Hats" cartoon is brilliant! There is nothing out there like it.
- Mary Ann C.

I loved your cartoon today. My wife is a retired teacher, both my daughters are teachers and my son-in-law is a teacher. So, I fully understand the perils and problems of teachers. Thank you for standing up for them.
- Dale M.

I love your cartoons. You make more sense than most politicians. - Candace S.

CARTOONIST AT WORK.

"This week's campaign donor list has arrived, Congressman,
along with updated instructions on how to vote."

141

_"We are politicians, and we didn't come to Washington to be treated like teachers."_

THIS IS OUR COUNTRY - NOT YOUR CHURCH.

"*The good news is we still have our base, the people you can fool all of the time.*"

*Hawaiian without a punch.*

*Miles was always looking for an edge in an uncertain world.*

*"If it was easy Mrs. Sugarman, everyone would be well-adjusted."*

# Want to Change the World?

**Start by using your turn signals.**

*"The test results confirm that, yes, your genes make you look fat.*
*So, you can stop asking."*

*"That's Jerome, he's a rescue."*

*"Stop believing everything you think."*

*Swiss army phone.*

"Hmm...Now how in the world is he going to read
that newspaper when it's all rolled up?"

*Inner Debate Team Practice.*

*Her family and friends loved Emmett and never
once gave her a hard time about being hobosexual.*

# ABOUT GRAHAM

Graham is a prolific artist, writer and author best known for his cartoons and humorous illustrations that have appeared in advertisements, newspapers, books, on greeting cards, clothing and licensed products world-wide since the 1980's.

His clients have included, the *NY Times, NY Newsday, Funny Times, AT&T, Prudential, Allstate, Adweek, NY Magazine, Club Med, Absolut, Citibank, Forbes, Money, Scholastic,* various publishers, fortune 500 companies and many others. His political cartoons and his acclaimed series, "Men In Hats" was featured in *The Commercial Appeal* of Memphis, TN, one of the nation's oldest papers.

Graham was born in Detroit and grew up in Elmira, NY. He attended the College of Wooster and went to Parsons School of Design in NYC where he studied advertising. He began selling his art on the street and soon built a successful freelance business. His T-shirt company, 90 Degree Angle, produced and sold his work world wide. His famous "NY Gun" shirt is still a New York City icon.

Graham is the creator of Boneless Chuck the beloved character/toy loved around the world, and Club Crib the infant clothing. Graham is also the author of *What Women Want: A Gentleman's Guide to Romance* and the soon-to-be released, *Win at Work Without Losing at Love.*

After decades in New York and Los Angeles, Graham now lives in Memphis, TN.

Made in the USA
Columbia, SC
29 March 2019